Alan Ridout

A Day in the Country

Twelve easy pieces with piano accompaniment for

Treble Recorder

THE ASSOCIATED BOARD OF
THE ROYAL SCHOOLS OF MUSIC

CONTENTS

A DAY IN THE COUNTRY
1 Starting out for a walk

G2

**TREBLE
RECORDER**

ALAN RIDOUT

2 Lingering by the wayside

91

3 Up and down hill

G2

4 Whistling to the sky

5 Strolling through woods

GI

6 Stepping out along a road

7 Resting by a lake

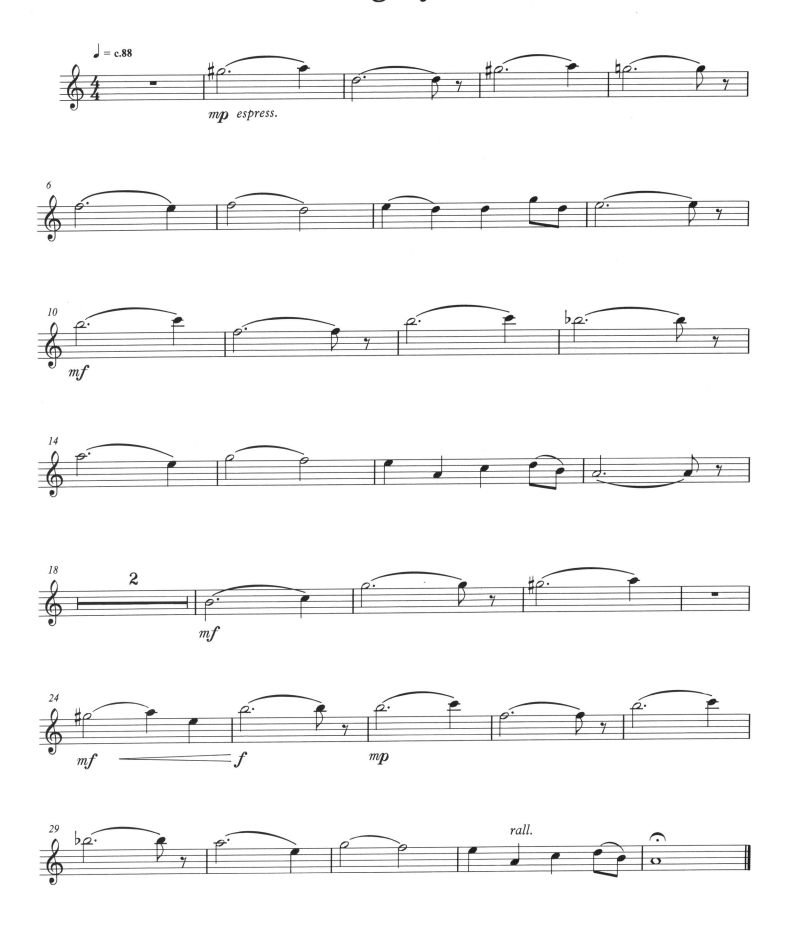

8 Crossing a bridge

9 Exploring a stream

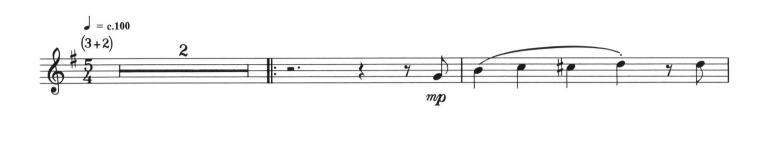

G 3

10 Running round a field

G2

11 Lazing in the sun

12 Returning home

1 Starting out for a walk

ALAN RIDOUT

AB 2181

2 Lingering by the wayside

3 Up and down hill

4 Whistling to the sky

5 Strolling through woods

10

6 Stepping out along a road

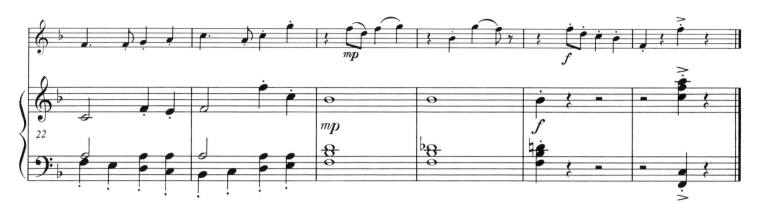

7 Resting by a lake

8 Crossing a bridge

9 Exploring a stream

10 Running round a field

11 Lazing in the sun

12 Returning home

Printed in England by Caligraving Limited Thetford Norfolk　　　AB 2181　　　4:03